This is a true story
about two baby gorillas
and their friend Debbie Freed.
Mopie and Hodari are lowland gorillas
who are growing up in the Bronx Zoo.
Debbie helps to feed the two babies
and joins in the gorilla games.

GAMES
GORILLAS PLAY

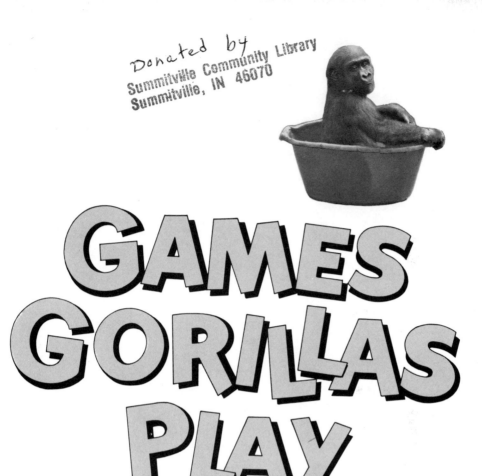

GAMES GORILLAS PLAY

Story by Kathy Darling

with Debbie Freed

Zoo pictures by Brian Ray and Angelo Calcaterra

GARRARD PUBLISHING COMPANY
CHAMPAIGN, ILLINOIS

Copyright © 1976 by Kathy Darling. All rights reserved. Manufactured in the U.S.A.
International Standard Book Number: 0-8116-4302-6
Library of Congress Catalog Card Number: 76-17324

Hodari is looking
for his friend Debbie.

Mopie is looking for Debbie too.

The gorilla babies are happy.
Debbie has come
to play with them.

The playground
is fun for gorillas.
This is where
they play games.

Mopie shows
how he can swing.
This is a good gorilla game.

Hodari and Debbie watch.

Mopie knows a better game.
He picks up a toy.

He climbs to the top.

He gets in the toy.

Mopie comes down.

He has found something.

He wants Debbie to see it.

What is it?

It is a leaf.

Hodari does not want
to play with the leaf.
He takes Debbie's hat.

Hodari runs away.

Mopie chases Hodari.

Hodari drops the hat.

He is afraid of Mopie.

He hides in the toy.

Debbie is happy
to have her hat back.
She gives Mopie a ride.

Mopie climbs up on a toy.
He is going
to jump on Hodari.

Mopie bites Hodari.

Mopie is sorry.

He and Hodari make up.

What can two gorillas play next?

Ball is a good gorilla game.
But only Hodari
wants to play.

Mopie wants
to take off Debbie's shoe.

It's time for a drink.

Gorillas like milk.

Hodari drinks all of his.

Mopie looks in the cup.
He wants to be sure
there is none left.

Hodari is in the tree.

He wants to play hide-and-seek.

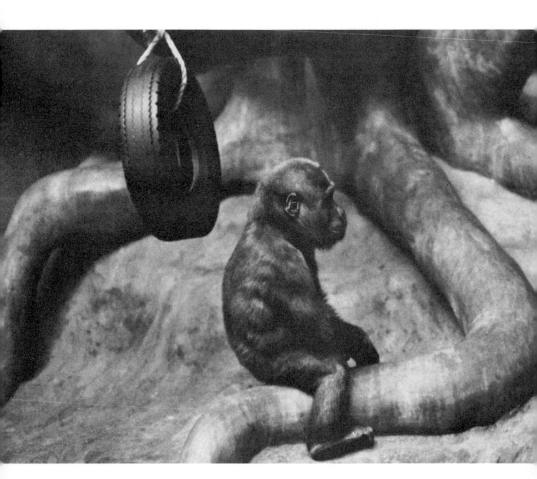

Debbie takes Mopie
to the tree.
Hodari is hiding there.

Where can he be?

Here he is!
Let's play tag.

29

Hodari runs up the tree.

Mopie doesn't want
to climb the tree.

Mopie wants to paint.

He paints with his fingers.

Mopie paints
with his left hand.

Sometimes he paints
with his right hand.

This is a picture that Mopie painted.

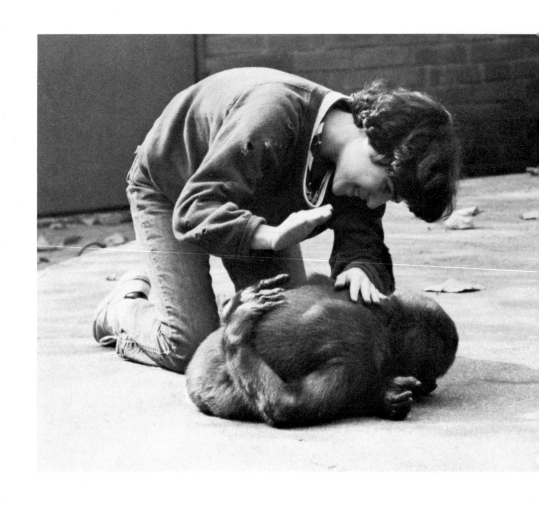

While Mopie paints,
Debbie plays pat-on-the-back
with Hodari.

Sometimes she tickles Mopie.
Mopie loves it!

Hodari likes
to be tickled too.

Debbie makes funny faces
so Hodari will smile.

Game time is over.
Mopie hugs Debbie good-bye.

Hodari hugs her too.